The Pear

The focus in this book is on the graphemes

ear, air, are

bear   pear

air   stairs

scared   carefully

near year ear disappeared

A pear tree grew in the garden at Follifoot Farm. Its branches reached the bedroom window. The tree had plenty of pears on it every year.

A monkey bear was often left on the bedroom windowsill. It looked out of the window at the tree full of pears.

One day, when the window was open, a gust of wind caught the bear. Whoosh! The bear flew into the pear tree.

The bear fell in between some branches. It got stuck there. The children at the farmhouse thought it was lost.

Then one day Jelly was chasing a squirrel. The squirrel ran up the pear tree. Jelly followed it, but it disappeared high up in the branches

While she was looking for the squirrel, Jelly saw the lost monkey bear. She thought that she would rescue it for the children.

She got hold of the bear by its ear and pulled it free from the branches. The branches wobbled. Oh no! Jelly was scared.

Jelly looked down. Oh no! She was high up in the air. She was scared. How would she get down?

Then she had a good idea. She very carefully went along the branch towards the open bedroom window. When she was near it she jumped ...

.... and landed on the bed. She put the bear on the pillow. Then she went down the stairs and back out into the garden.

Vowel graphemes

ay/a-e:	day chasing
ee/ea:	tree free between reached
y/i-e/igh:	by while high
ow/o:	window windowsill followed pillow open hold
oo:	whoosh bedroom
ew/ue:	grew flew rescue
oo:	looked good Follifoot looking
ow/ou:	down how out farmhouse
or:	for
ar:	garden farm farmhouse
aw:	saw
are/air/ear:	scared carefully stairs air pear bear
ear:	year ear disappeared near